A Boy, a Bug, and a Bear
play hide-and-seek.

The Bear is big.
The Bug and
the Boy always
find him.

The Boy is smaller than
the Bear.
Sometimes the Bug and
the Bear find the Boy.

Sometimes they do not.

The Bug is little.

The Bear and Boy do not
find the Bug.

They take a nap instead.
Good night, Boy.
Good night, Bear.